Delight in the Lord

MAKING YOUR HOME a haven

A 4-WEEK BIBLE STUDY

by Courtney Joseph

Welcome to Good Morning Girls! We are so glad you are joining us.

God created us to walk with Him, to know Him, and to be loved by Him. He is our living well, and when we drink from the water He continually provides, His living water will change the entire course of our lives.

> *Jesus said: "Whoever drinks of the water that I will give him will never be thirsty again. The water that I will give him will become in him a spring of water welling up to eternal life." ~ John 4:14 (ESV)*

So let's begin.

The method we use here at GMG is called the **SOAK** method.

- ❒ **S**—The S stands for *Scripture*—Read the chapter for the day. Then choose 1-2 verses and write them out word for word. (There is no right or wrong choice—just let the Holy Spirit guide you.)

- ❒ **O**—The O stands for *Observation*—Look at the verse or verses you wrote out. Write 1 or 2 observations. What stands out to you? What do you learn about the character of God from these verses? Is there a promise, command or teaching?

- ❒ **A**—The A stands for *Application*—Personalize the verses. What is God saying to you? How can you apply them to your life? Are there any changes you need to make or an action to take?

- ❒ **K**—The K stands for *Kneeling in Prayer*—Pause, kneel and pray. Confess any sin God has revealed to you today. Praise God for His word. Pray the passage over your own life or someone you love. Ask God to help you live out your applications.

SOAK God's word into your heart and squeeze every bit of nourishment you can out of each day's scripture reading. Soon you will find your life transformed by the renewing of your mind!

Walk with the King!

Courtney

WomenLivingWell.org, GoodMorningGirls.org

Join the GMG Community

WomenLivingWell.org | GoodMorningGirls.org

Facebook.com/WomenLivingwell | Facebook.com/GoodMorningGirlsWLW

Instagram.com/WomenLivingWell #WomenLivingWell

#MakingYourHomeAHaven

COLORS	KEYWORDS
PURPLE	God, Jesus, Holy Spirit, Saviour, Messiah
PINK	women of the Bible, family, marriage, parenting, friendship, relationships
RED	love, kindness, mercy, compassion, peace, grace
GREEN	faith, obedience, growth, fruit, salvation, fellowship, repentance
YELLOW	worship, prayer, praise, doctrine, angels, miracles, power of God, blessings
BLUE	wisdom, teaching, instruction, commands
ORANGE	prophecy, history, times, places, kings, genealogies, people, numbers, covenants, vows, visions, oaths, future
BROWN/GRAY	Satan, sin, death, hell, evil, idols, false teachers, hypocrisy, temptation

TABLE OF CONTENTS

INTRODUCTION

Welcome to the *Making Your Home a Haven* Bible Study! Eleven years ago, I began this series online at WomenLivingWell.org. Never could I have imagined how much it would resonate with so many women around the world. I pray this study blesses you in the same way!

If you have been feeling disconnected from God or if you have a desire to go deeper in your walk with the Lord, then this study is for you.

God's pace is much slower than this world's pace.

We must slow down to catch up with God.

We must create calm moments in our day because it's in the unhurried moments that we can clearly see and hear the voice of God.

This Bible Study is going to help you slow down. It is going to force you to pause every day and enter into the presence of our Almighty God through thanksgiving, prayer and the reading of God's Word.

Self-care is a very popular concept these days, but I believe that soul care IS self-care. So, let's take care of our souls by intentionally creating a physical environment in our homes, as well as a spiritual environment, that brings us closer to God. As a result, we will experience peace and a sense of calmness inside our souls, no matter what we are facing.

Each week, I will provide for you a practical challenge of something I do in my home that makes it more of a haven. I hope you will take the challenges. They do make a difference!

Each weekday, we will pause, give thanks, pray and meditate on God's Word through SOAKing in the daily scripture reading for the day.

Also, online at WomenLivingWell.org, you will find four videos—one per week—that correspond with the scriptures we are studying.

I encourage you to give yourself permission to not have your to-do list all checked off in order for you to slow down and catch up with God.

David writes in Psalm 42:1, 2:

> *"As the deer pants for streams of water,*
> *so my soul pants for you, my God.*
> *² My soul thirsts for God, for the living God.*
> *When can I go and meet with God?"*

I pray that your time spent in God's Word will bless your soul and quench your thirst and that you will live well, as you drink from the living well, the living words of God. (John 4:13-14)

I can't wait to take this journey with you!

Keep Walking with the King,

Courtney

Week 1: Delight

Rejoice in the Lord always; I will say it again, rejoice.

Philippians 4:4

When our schedules are full and our to-do lists are overwhelming, it's hard to stop and enjoy life to the fullest. Because of Jesus' death on the cross and the forgiveness of our sins, we have a personal relationship with God. Not only should we delight in God as our savior and friend, but God is also a giver of good gifts, that he wants us to delight in!

So how do we delight in the Lord and the good gifts he has given us?

We must stop.

We must stop and open our eyes to the generosity of our God. When we sit still in his presence and simply enjoy the Lord, we find that our souls can be satisfied in him. He is a delight to know!

Once we are still in God's presence and delighting in him, the fullness and richness of all God has given us, comes to life. Suddenly we see God's hand in everything. We see God's love in the chirping birds, a crispy apple, a hot cup of coffee, a bouquet of flowers, a hug from a friend, a beautiful sunset, a powerful storm and the changing leaves on the trees.

People who work too much, don't delight in life. Instead of experiencing freedom in Christ, they lack the self-control and faith to simply stop, rest and delight. Every evening the sun sets, signaling it is time to rest. And on the seventh day of creation, God rested. Rest and delight are God given, built-in needs for our souls.

So, it's time! It's time to take 15 minutes a day to stop and be grateful, pray, meditate and delight in the Lord and then go forward with the day, delighting in the good gifts God has given us to enjoy. Let's get started.

WEEK 1 CHALLENGE

Go buy an extra-large candle and light your candle every day in your home. Each time the glimmer of the candle catches your eye, stop, pray and give thanks.

I will be starting my candle in the morning, but you can start yours at dinnertime or whenever is convenient for you. I will be placing mine in the kitchen—the main hub of my home.

{Share your pictures of your candle on Instagram by using the hashtags: #MakingYourHomeAHaven and #WomenLivingWell}

DAY 1

Rejoice in the Lord always; I will say it again, rejoice.

Philippians 4:4

Things I Am Grateful for Today:

_____

_____

_____

_____

_____

_____

_____

Things I Am Praying for Today:

_____

_____

_____

_____

_____

_____

_____

_____

S—The S stands for **Scripture**

O—The O stands for **Observation**

A—The A stands for **Application**

K—The K stands for **Kneeling in Prayer**

DAY 2

You make known to me the path of life, in your presence there is fullness of joy;
at your right hand are pleasures forevermore.

Psalm 16:11

Things I Am Grateful for Today:

_____

_____

_____

_____

_____

_____

_____

_____

Things I Am Praying for Today:

_____

_____

_____

_____

_____

_____

_____

_____

Psalm 16:1~11

S—The S stands for **Scripture**

O—The O stands for **Observation**

A—The A stands for **Application**

K—The K stands for **Kneeling in Prayer**

DAY 3

Delight yourself in the Lord, And he will give you the desires of your heart.

Psalm 37:4

Things I Am Grateful for Today:

_____

_____

_____

_____

_____

_____

_____

Things I Am Praying for Today:

_____

_____

_____

_____

_____

_____

_____

S—The S stands for *Scripture*

O—The O stands for *Observation*

A—The A stands for *Application*

K—The K stands for *Kneeling in Prayer*

DAY 4

*Let the word of Christ dwell in you richly, teaching and admonishing
one another in all wisdom, singing psalms and hymns and spiritual songs,
with thankfulness in your hearts to God.*

Colossians 3:16

Things I Am Grateful for Today:

_____

_____

_____

_____

_____

_____

_____

Things I Am Praying for Today:

_____

_____

_____

_____

_____

_____

_____

_____

S—The S stands for **_Scripture_**

O—The O stands for **_Observation_**

A—The A stands for **_Application_**

K—The K stands for **_Kneeling in Prayer_**

DAY 5

Praise the Lord! For it is good to sing praises to our God;
for it is pleasant, and a song of praise is fitting.

Psalm 147:1

Things I Am Grateful for Today:

_____

_____

_____

_____

_____

_____

_____

_____

Things I Am Praying for Today:

_____

_____

_____

_____

_____

_____

_____

_____

Psalm 147:1-20

S—The S stands for **Scripture**

O—The O stands for **Observation**

A—The A stands for **Application**

K—The K stands for **Kneeling in Prayer**

Week 2: Draw Near

The Lord is near.

Philippians 4:5

Our relationship with God is meant to be so much more than just a quick 15-minute quiet time. We must go deeper. Our souls need to drink deeply from God's living well. We must stop what we are doing and draw near to God.

When was the last time you sat quietly before the Lord in silence?

Our world is noisy. In order to listen and hear from God, we may need to change our location. Perhaps we need to go outside, go for a walk or shut the door to our bedroom and be alone. As we draw near to God, the invisible becomes visible.

Sometimes as we are silent before the Lord, he reveals things in our lives we need to deal with. Busyness tends to drown out the voice of God, but silence is a megaphone. When we take the time to be vulnerable before the Lord, he speaks.

As we listen and pray and read scripture, we commune with the God of the universe and we grow in intimacy with him. We experience the assurance that we are loved, and the reality of eternity comes alive. There is no greater delight than knowing God and experiencing him!

When was the last time you sat alone and sang a song to God?

The book of Psalms is the longest book of the Bible and it's a book of songs. God delights in the praise of his people! In Psalm 100, we are told to shout for joy, worship with gladness, come before God with joyful songs, and give thanks for the Lord is good and his love endures forever. Let's do that this week, as we draw near to God.

¹ Shout for joy to the Lord, all the earth.
²Worship the Lord with gladness;
come before him with joyful songs.
³Know that the Lord is God.
It is he who made us, and we are his;
we are his people, the sheep of his pasture.
⁴Enter his gates with thanksgiving
and his courts with praise;
give thanks to him and praise his name.
⁵For the Lord is good and his love endures forever;
his faithfulness continues through all generations.
—Psalm 100:1-5

WEEK 2 CHALLENGE

Keep your candle going and add to it—soft music every day in your home. Choose worship, classical or another form of peaceful music that helps you focus on the Lord.

My candle and soft music literally change the atmosphere of my home. While the rest of my home may be messy, my candle keeps on burning and my soft music keeps on playing. Morning, noon and night they serve me. My candle serves me with a flickering warm light, a pleasant scent, and a reminder to turn to God as my source of strength and help. My music serves me with a soothing sound. They don't make messes, they don't need managed, they just simply bless me and my family. I hope it blesses you too.

{Share your pictures of your favorite Worship CD or playlist on Instagram by using the hashtags: #MakingYourHomeAHaven and #WomenLivingWell}

DAY 1

The Lord is near.

Philippians 4:5

Things I Am Grateful for Today:

_____

_____

_____

_____

_____

_____

_____

_____

Things I Am Praying for Today:

_____

_____

_____

_____

_____

_____

_____

_____

S—The S stands for **Scripture**

O—The O stands for **Observation**

A—The A stands for **Application**

K—The K stands for **Kneeling in Prayer**

DAY 2

And without faith it is impossible to please him, for whoever would draw near to God must believe that he exists and that he rewards those who seek him.

Hebrews 11:6

Things I Am Grateful for Today:

_____

_____

_____

_____

_____

_____

_____

Things I Am Praying for Today:

_____

_____

_____

_____

_____

_____

_____

_____

S—The S stands for **Scripture**

O—The O stands for **Observation**

A—The A stands for **Application**

K—The K stands for **Kneeling in Prayer**

DAY 3

Draw near to God, and he will draw near to you.

James 4:8

Things I Am Grateful for Today:

_____

_____

_____

_____

_____

_____

Things I Am Praying for Today:

_____

_____

_____

_____

_____

_____

_____

S—The S stands for *Scripture*

O—The O stands for *Observation*

A—The A stands for *Application*

K—The K stands for *Kneeling in Prayer*

DAY 4

*Let us then with confidence draw near to the throne of grace,
that we may receive mercy and find grace to help in time of need.*

Hebrews 4:16

Things I Am Grateful for Today:

_____

_____

_____

_____

_____

_____

_____

_____

Things I Am Praying for Today:

_____

_____

_____

_____

_____

_____

_____

_____

S—The S stands for **Scripture**

O—The O stands for **Observation**

A—The A stands for **Application**

K—The K stands for **Kneeling in Prayer**

DAY 5

God is our refuge and strength, a very present help in trouble.

Psalm 46:1

Things I Am Grateful for Today:

_____

_____

_____

_____

_____

_____

_____

_____

Things I Am Praying for Today:

_____

_____

_____

_____

_____

_____

_____

_____

Psalm 46:1~10

S—The S stands for **Scripture**

O—The O stands for **Observation**

A—The A stands for **Application**

K—The K stands for **Kneeling in Prayer**

Week 3: Desires

Do not be anxious about anything, but in every situation, by prayer and petition, with thanksgiving, present your requests to God.

Philippians 4:6

We all have two worlds to balance, our outer world and our inner world. The outer world throws a lot our way, with high highs and low lows. One day our dreams may be coming true and the next, we could be facing our worst nightmare. God wants us to experience peace and joy in our lives no matter what our circumstances are. In difficult times, if we hold tightly to the wrong things, our inner world will become anxious and fearful.

We were made to be connected to God. Our soul needs to be anchored to Christ but sin in our lives leads to a disconnect. When we desire things that are contrary to God's desires for us, our soul drifts.

When was the last time you confessed your sins to the Lord?

Pause. Give your soul a good cleanse right now, by confessing any sins you are struggling with. God is faithful and just to forgive your sins and cleanse you from all unrighteousness. (1 John 1:9)

Are you anxious or worried about anything in your outer world right now?

God wants us to have peace and he tells us the way to get there is by turning our worries over to him, by prayer and petition.

What is prayer? Prayer is simply talking to God.

What is petition? It is making a request of God and usually it is something we strongly desire.

Sometimes we can look at prayer as a duty that is draining. We'd rather do something fun or something that seems more productive in the outer world, to solve our problems. But God knows that taking time to be still and pray over our worries and desires is what is best for us.

It is life giving!

So, this week, let's practice the presence of God every single day. Let's bring our outer world and inner world into harmony through prayer. God loves you and is with you and he wants to hear from you.

WEEK 3 CHALLENGE

Go pick a bouquet of flowers from your garden or a nearby field or buy yourself a small bouquet. Each time you see the flowers, be reminded of God's love and presence with you. Our creator God is listening to your prayers.

I will be purchasing a small bouquet from my grocery store and placing it in a vase, in my kitchen.

{Share your pictures of your flowers on Instagram by using the hashtags: #MakingYourHomeAHaven and #WomenLivingWell}

DAY 1

Do not be anxious about anything, but in every situation, by prayer and petition, with thanksgiving, present your requests to God.

Philippians 4:6

Things I Am Grateful for Today:

_____

_____

_____

_____

_____

_____

_____

Things I Am Praying for Today:

_____

_____

_____

_____

_____

_____

_____

S—The S stands for **Scripture**

O—The O stands for **Observation**

A—The A stands for **Application**

K—The K stands for **Kneeling in Prayer**

DAY 2

But when you pray, go into your room and shut the door and pray to your Father who is in secret. And your Father who sees in secret will reward you.

Matthew 6:6

Things I Am Grateful for Today:

_____

_____

_____

_____

_____

_____

_____

_____

Things I Am Praying for Today:

_____

_____

_____

_____

_____

_____

_____

_____

S—The S stands for **Scripture**

O—The O stands for **Observation**

A—The A stands for **Application**

K—The K stands for **Kneeling in Prayer**

DAY 3

Walk by the Spirit, and you will not gratify the desires of the flesh.

Galatians 5:16

Things I Am Grateful for Today:

_____

_____

_____

_____

_____

_____

_____

Things I Am Praying for Today:

_____

_____

_____

_____

_____

_____

_____

S—The S stands for *Scripture*

O—The O stands for *Observation*

A—The A stands for *Application*

K—The K stands for *Kneeling in Prayer*

DAY 4

*Rejoice always, pray without ceasing, give thanks in all circumstances;
for this is the will of God in Christ Jesus for you.*

1 Thessalonians 5:16~18

Things I Am Grateful for Today:

_____

_____

_____

_____

_____

_____

_____

_____

Things I Am Praying for Today:

_____

_____

_____

_____

_____

_____

_____

_____

S—The S stands for **Scripture**

O—The O stands for **Observation**

A—The A stands for **Application**

K—The K stands for **Kneeling in Prayer**

DAY 5

Delight yourself in the Lord, and he will give you the desires of your heart.

Psalm 37:4

Things I Am Grateful for Today:

_____

_____

_____

_____

_____

_____

_____

Things I Am Praying for Today:

_____

_____

_____

_____

_____

_____

_____

Psalm 37:4~9

S—The S stands for **Scripture**

O—The O stands for **Observation**

A—The A stands for **Application**

K—The K stands for **Kneeling in Prayer**

Week 4: Dependence

*And the peace of God, which surpasses all understanding,
will guard your hearts and your minds in Christ Jesus*

Philippians 4:7

To depend on God is to rely solely on him. When we trust in God, we release our worries and fears to him and in return we experience a deep peace, that is beyond understanding.

We are not saved by works. We are not saved through our prayer life and we are not saved by reading the Bible. We are saved by trusting in Jesus' work on the cross for the forgiveness of our sins. At the core of our faith, is a deep trust and dependence on God. But it seems that after salvation, we have a tendency to get busy serving and striving. Instead of depending on God, we live as if everything depends on us and slowly, we end up drawn away from God.

In Psalm 1:1-3, we are told that a man who is blessed is "like a tree planted by streams of water that yields its fruit in its season and its leaf does not wither. In all that he does, he prospers."

Where have you planted yourself?

Are you depending on God or are you trying to dig your own wells for water?

Going your own way for a while feels good, but the temporal things of this world will always leave your soul unsatisfied and desiring more. God is our living water and when we plant ourselves by his living water, our inner roots will run deep and we will be strong.

Our relationship with God is more than a devotional—it's living with devotion and total dependence on him. We can only experience his peace, when we are trusting that he loves us and is taking care of us.

It takes faith to rest. It takes faith to trust and it takes faith to depend on God. So, let's be intentional this week and stop striving and start resting in God. Draw near to him, delight in him and let him exchange your desires in your heart, for the desires that he has for you.

Keep walking with the King!

WEEK 4 CHALLENGE

Seek out a place of solitude to get alone with God. Stop your work, turn off your phone, the television, music and computer. Be still. Go outside or find a place in your home, where you can be alone and simply rest and be at peace. Practice the presence of God.

Rest is a need—not a want. Rest is not optional or something we wait to do when we are retired. Rest is a blessing from the Lord, and it requires humility to admit we need it. I'll be running a bubble bath and probably taking a much-needed nap this week. Soul care is self-care. So, enjoy it!

{Share your pictures of your favorite place to rest on Instagram by using the hashtags: #MakingYourHomeAHaven and #WomenLivingWell}

DAY 1

And the peace of God, which surpasses all understanding,
will guard your hearts and your minds in Christ Jesus.

Philippians 4:7

Things I Am Grateful for Today:

_____

_____

_____

_____

_____

_____

_____

Things I Am Praying for Today:

_____

_____

_____

_____

_____

_____

_____

_____

S—The S stands for *Scripture*

O—The O stands for *Observation*

A—The A stands for *Application*

K—The K stands for *Kneeling in Prayer*

DAY 2

*Mary sat at the Lord's feet and listened to his teaching
but Martha was distracted with much serving.*

Luke 10:39~40

Things I Am Grateful for Today:

_____

_____

_____

_____

_____

_____

_____

Things I Am Praying for Today:

_____

_____

_____

_____

_____

_____

_____

_____

S—The S stands for **Scripture**

O—The O stands for **Observation**

A—The A stands for **Application**

K—The K stands for **Kneeling in Prayer**

DAY 3

You keep him in perfect peace whose mind is stayed on you,
Because he trusts in you.

Isaiah 26:3

Things I Am Grateful for Today:

_____

_____

_____

_____

_____

_____

_____

Things I Am Praying for Today:

_____

_____

_____

_____

_____

_____

_____

_____

S—The S stands for **Scripture**

O—The O stands for **Observation**

A—The A stands for **Application**

K—The K stands for **Kneeling in Prayer**

DAY 4

Come to me, all who are weary and burdened, and I will give you rest.

Matthew 11:28

Things I Am Grateful for Today:

_____

_____

_____

_____

_____

_____

_____

_____

Things I Am Praying for Today:

_____

_____

_____

_____

_____

_____

_____

_____

S—The S stands for *Scripture*

O—The O stands for *Observation*

A—The A stands for *Application*

K—The K stands for *Kneeling in Prayer*

DAY 5

He restores my soul.

Psalm 23:3

Things I Am Grateful for Today:

_____

_____

_____

_____

_____

_____

_____

_____

Things I Am Praying for Today:

_____

_____

_____

_____

_____

_____

_____

_____

Psalm 23:1~6

S—The S stands for **Scripture**

O—The O stands for **Observation**

A—The A stands for **Application**

K—The K stands for **Kneeling in Prayer**

Video Notes

(go to WomenLivingWell.org to find the weekly corresponding videos)